THE GREAT GARDEN ADVENTURE

THE GREAT GARDEN ADVENTURE

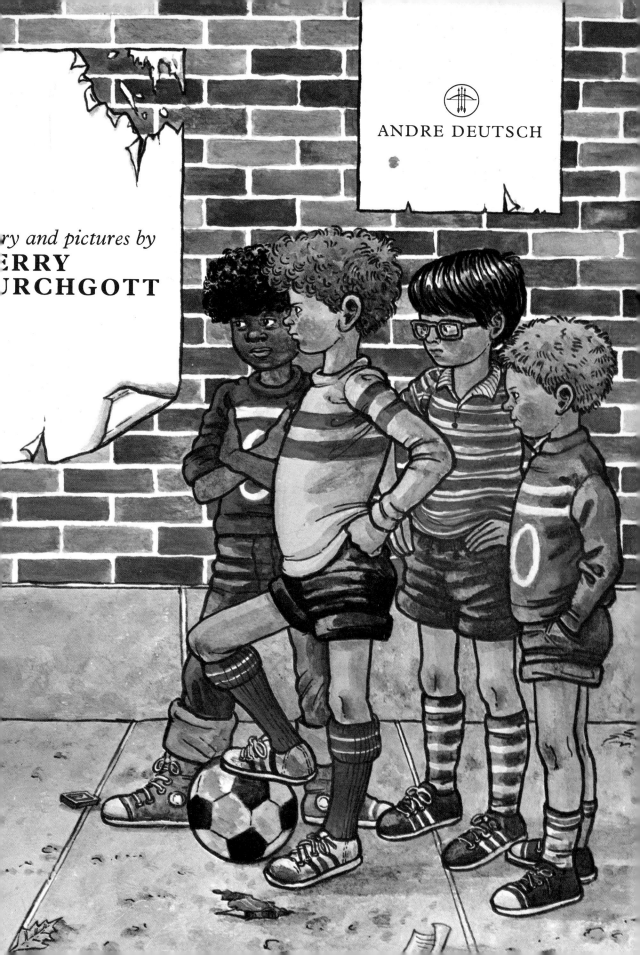

First published 1978 by
André Deutsch Limited
105 Great Russell Street London WCI

Copyright © 1978 by Terry Furchgott
Printed in Great Britain by
Sackville Press Billericay Ltd

British Library Cataloguing in Publication Data

Furchgott, Terry
   The great garden adventure.
   I. Title
   823'.9'IJ

   ISBN 0-233-96988-8

Amanda and Daisy were sisters. They lived with their mother in a small flat in the centre of a big city. Their mother, who wasn't very rich, went out to work every day and didn't get home until tea time.

After school Amanda, who was older, walked Daisy home and looked after her. Usually, they played on the pavement in front of their block of flats. But sometimes a ginger-haired boy named Freddy, and his gang, took over the entire pavement for games of football.

The first time this happened, Amanda asked Freddy
if she could play too. But he just laughed and said,
"Don't be silly. Girls can't play football."

"So much for you, then," Amanda answered.
"Daisy and I have plenty of other things to do." And
off they went to play their own games.

Amanda and Daisy's favourite times were evenings and weekends, when their mother was home from work. Sometimes she told them stories about when she was a girl and lived in the country. "If only we had a back garden here," she would say with a sigh, "we could grow vegetables as my father did, and maybe even save money on food bills." Amanda and Daisy thought it would be great fun to grow things in a proper garden.

One day after school, Amanda and Daisy were
playing jungle explorers. "Look out!" cried Amanda.
"There's a lion about to attack!" And off they ran,
into an alley, through a gate, under a fence, and . . .

. . . suddenly they found themselves in a large open space. It was surrounded by a high fence which cut out any sight or sound of the city.

"Where are we?" asked Daisy.

"I don't know," said Amanda. "We're explorers aren't we? Look, there's a shed over there. Let's investigate it."

The door of the shed was rusted shut, but, after much pulling and tugging, it creaked open and a pile of old tools fell out. "We learned about these at school," said Daisy. "You use them in the garden."

Suddenly Amanda had a wonderful idea. "Let's make our *own* garden here," she said. "There's plenty of room, and now we even have tools. We can grow things to eat, then Mum won't have to worry about money. It'll be fun. But we must keep it a secret, especially from Freddy and his gang, or else they'll want this place for a football pitch."

"Okay," promised Daisy, "but do we know how to grow food?"

"Not really," said Amanda. "We'll get a book on gardening from the library."

"And we must buy some seeds," added Daisy. "I know we need them."

So off they ran, stopping first at their flat to collect
their money.

Then on to the library where they took out a book
called *How to Garden in Six Easy Steps* by Mr. P. P.
Cabbage.

Next they went around the corner to the supermarket, where, in the gardening section, there were hundreds of beautiful seed packets. They chose lettuce, radishes, carrots, peas, beans and beetroot. They also bought some sunflower seeds (their mother loved sunflowers), a packet of daisy seeds for Daisy, and one each of nasturtiums and petunias, because they looked pretty. They paid for the seeds, it took all their money. Then back they ran to the secret place.

"Right," said Amanda, opening the book at page one. But, before she could say another word, through the hole in the fence burst Freddy and his gang.

"Ha ha, we followed you. Ha ha, we followed you," they chanted. Freddy looked around. "Hey gang," he said, "this wouldn't make a bad practice pitch. Let's have a game." He kicked the football he was holding into the air, and, turning to run, bumped into Daisy and knocked her down. She began to cry.

Amanda suddenly grew very angry. Walking up to Freddy she said, "Now see what you've done, you big bully. Barging in here with your dumb gang. This is our place, we found it and you're not invited. Go away!" And she gave him such a push that he sat down hard in a big mud puddle.

Freddy looked so funny sitting in the mud that the rest of his gang, and even Daisy, roared with laughter.

"What are these for, Amanda?" asked one of the boys, picking up the packet of lettuce seeds.

"Yeah, and where did you get all these tools?" asked another.

"Daisy and I are going to have a garden here," said Amanda. "We're going to grow flowers and masses of vegetables to eat at home. Maybe we'll even sell some and make lots of money."

The boys looked interested. "Listen, Amanda," said Freddy who had picked himself up. "This idea sounds all right. But, if you let us join in, we could grow twice as much stuff."

"All right," agreed Amanda, "but Daisy and I had the idea and paid for the seeds. You can help, but we're in charge."

"Right then," said Freddy, "it's a deal."

"Hooray!" cried the boys. "Three cheers for the Garden Gang."

Every day after that the Gang met at the secret place, and followed the instructions in *How to Garden in Six Easy Steps.*

Step One was: "Prepare the Ground". While doing this, they discovered some blackberry bushes and two old apple trees.

Step Two was: "Sow the Seeds".

Step Three was: "Water the Garden".

Step Four was: "Weed the Garden".

Finally, one day Amanda read out Step Five: "Pick the flowers and vegetables". By tea time the Garden Gang had collected all the lettuces, carrots, beets, peas, beans, nasturtiums, daisies, petunias, and sunflowers. They also picked all the blackberries and apples they could reach.

"What do you think we should do now, Amanda?" Freddy asked. "There's far too much here for just us."

"Let's take it to the supermarket and sell it," said Amanda.

So they piled everything into boxes, and baskets, and wagons, and wheelbarrows, keeping plenty for their own mothers. Then off they went to the supermarket, where the manager was delighted to buy such beautiful produce.

Amanda divided the money he gave them equally
between the members of the Garden Gang. Then they
all said goodbye, and went home to tea.

Amanda and Daisy's mother was very pleased to receive the food, flowers and money. But she wanted to know how they had got it. So they told her everything that had happened. At the end of the story, she hugged them both and said, "My goodness, how clever of you to do all that. With all this money and food you've brought home, I think we can have a proper holiday together this year. But there's one more thing I want to know.

"Mr. P. P. Cabbage's book is called *How to Garden in Six Easy Steps*, but you only got to Step Five. What in the world can Step Six be?"

Amanda opened the book at the last page. "Step Number Six," she read out, "Eat your fruit and vegetables."

And that's just what they did.